Usborne
First Colouring Book
Football

Illustrated by

Annalisa Sanmartino
and Giulia Torelli

This book belongs to

‒‒‒‒‒‒‒‒‒‒‒‒‒‒‒‒‒‒‒‒‒‒‒‒‒‒‒‒‒‒‒‒‒‒

Words by Sam Taplin. Designed by Matt Durber and Keith Newell.

The players

These footballers are all from different teams.
Design a colourful kit for each one.

Goalkeeper

Striker

Left midfield

Striker

Centre midfield

Right back

Right midfield

Centre midfield

Central defence

Left back

Central defence

3

Match day

Are you ready for the big game? Colour your hat, scarf, shirt and lots of other things you might see when you go to cheer your team on at the stadium.

Beanie hat

Team scarf

Mascot

Tickets

Shirt

Socks

Snack bar

Football

Cap

Stadium

Drinks

Flags

Woolly hat

Tie

Mug

Sunglasses

Lunch box

Shorts

Team bus

On the training ground

A footballer needs to practise lots of different skills. Add colour to these training players.

Shooting

Passing

Tackling

Dribbling

Saving

Heading

Scoring!

Team badges

Every football team has a different badge on its shirt.
Colour these badges and make up a name for each team.

Corner kick

In this game, one team has won a corner. Colour all the players, and design a bright kit for the goalkeeper.

On the pitch

It's the middle of an exciting game. Work out who's on which team, then use different colours for each one.

Victory parade

This team are parading around town to show off a trophy they've won. Finish colouring the bus and the players.

CUP WINNERS

Fantastic fans

During a match, the fans roar and clap and cheer for their team. Give these fans bright scarves and shirts, and write a message on the banner.

Victory!

Colour the celebrating players and the trophy.

Use these stickers in any way you like.